Table of (

M000159922

Freezing and Boiling Point Graph

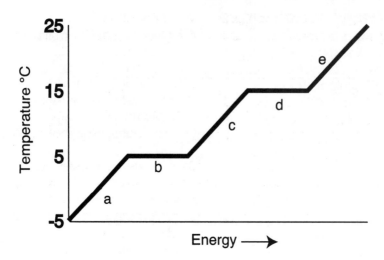

Answer the following questions using the chart above.

1. What is the freezing point of the substance? _____

2. What is the boiling point of the substance? _____

3. What is the melting point of the substance? _____

4. What letter represents the range where the solid is being warmed? _____

5. What letter represents the range where the liquid is being warmed? _____

6. What letter represents the range where the vapor is being warmed? _____

7. What letter represents the melting of the solid? _____

8. What letter represents the vaporization of the liquid? _____

9. What letter(s) shows a change in potential energy? _____

10. What letter(s) shows a change in kinetic energy? _____

11. What letter represents condensation? _____

12. What letter represents crystallization? _____

Heat and Its Measurement

Heat (or energy) can be measured in units of calories or joules. When there is a temperature change (ΔT), heat (Q) can be calculated using this formula:

$$Q = \text{mass} \times \Delta T \times \text{specific heat capacity}$$
$$(\Delta T = \text{Final Temp - Initial Temp})$$

During a phase change, we use this formula:

$$Q = \text{mass} \times \text{heat of fusion (or heat of vaporization)}$$

Solve the following problems.

1. How many joules of heat are given off when 5.0 g of water cool from 75° C to 25° C? (Specific heat of water = 4.18 j/g° C)

   _____

2. How many calories are given off by the water in Problem 1? (Specific heat of water = 1.0 cal/g° C)

   _____

3. How many joules does it take to melt 35 g of ice at 0° C? (heat of fusion = 333 j/g)

   _____

4. How many calories are given off when 85 g of steam condense to liquid water? (heat of vaporization = 539.4 cal/g)

   _____

5. How many joules of heat are necessary to raise the temperature of 25 g of water from 10° C to 60° C?

   _____

6. How many calories are given off when 50 g of water at 0° freezes? (heat of fusion = 79.72 cal/g)

   _____

Vapor Pressure and Boiling

A liquid will boil when its vapor pressure equals atmospheric pressure. Answer the questions following the graph.

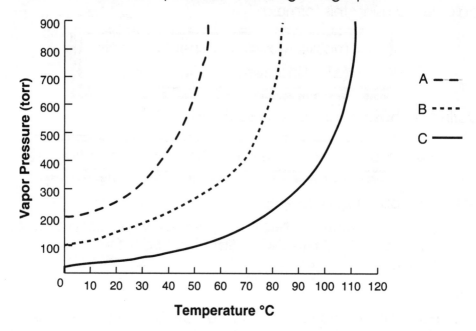

1. At what temperature would Liquid A boil at an atmospheric pressure of 400 torr? _____

2. Liquid B? _____

3. Liquid C? _____

4. How low must the atmospheric pressure be for Liquid A to boil at 35° C? _____

5. Liquid B? _____

6. Liquid C? _____

7. What is the normal boiling point of Liquid A? _____

8. Liquid B? _____

9. Liquid C? _____

10. Which liquid has the strongest intermolecular forces?

_____

Matter—Substances vs. Mixtures

All matter can be classified as either a substance (element or compound) or a mixture (heterogeneous or homogeneous).

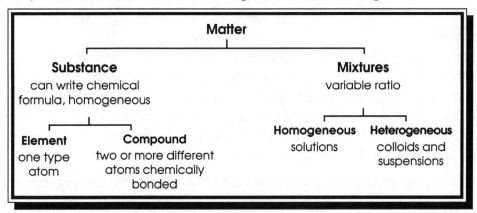

Classify each of the following as to whether it is a substance or a mixture. If it is a substance, write Element or Compound in the substance column. If it is a mixture, write Heterogeneous or Homogeneous in the mixture column.

Type of Matter	Substance	Mixture
1. chlorine		
2. water		
3. soil		
4. sugar water		
5. oxygen		
6. carbon dioxide		
7. rocky road ice cream		
8. alcohol		
9. pure air		
10. iron		

Physical vs. Chemical Properties

A physical property is observed with the senses and can be determined without destroying the object. For example, color, shape, mass, length and odor are all examples of physical properties.

A chemical property indicates how a substance reacts with something else. The original substance is fundamentally changed in observing a chemical property. For example, the ability of iron to rust is a chemical property. The iron has reacted with oxygen, and the original iron metal is changed. It now exists as iron oxide, a different substance.

Classify the following properties as either chemical or physical by putting a check in the appropriate column.

	Physical Property	Chemical Property
1. blue color		
2. density		
3. flammability		
4. solubility		
5. reacts with acid to form H_2		
6. supports combustion		
7. sour taste		
8. melting point		
9. reacts with water to form a gas		
10. reacts with a base to form water		
11. hardness		
12. boiling point		
13. can neutralize a base		
14. luster		
15. odor		

Physical vs. Chemical Changes

In a physical change, the original substance still exists, it has only changed in form. In a chemical change, a new substance is produced. Energy changes always accompany chemical changes.

Classify the following as being a physical or chemical change.

1. Sodium hydroxide dissolves in water. _____

2. Hydrochloric acid reacts with potassium hydroxide to produce a salt, water and heat. _____

3. A pellet of sodium is sliced in two. _____

4. Water is heated and changed to steam.

   _____

5. Potassium chlorate decomposes to potassium chloride and oxygen gas. _____

6. Iron rusts. _____

7. When placed in H_2O, a sodium pellet catches on fire as hydrogen gas is liberated and sodium hydroxide forms.

   _____

8. Evaporation _____

9. Ice melting _____

10. Milk sours. _____

11. Sugar dissolves in water. _____

12. Wood rotting _____

13. Pancakes cooking on a griddle _____

14. Grass growing in a lawn _____

15. A tire is inflated with air. _____

16. Food is digested in the stomach. _____

17. Water is absorbed by a paper towel. _____

Boyle's Law

Boyle's Law states that the volume of a gas varies inversely with its pressure if temperature is held constant. (If one goes up, the other goes down.) We use the formula:

$$P_1 \times V_1 = P_2 \times V_2$$

Solve the following problems (assuming constant temperature).

1. A sample of oxygen gas occupies a volume of 250. mL at 740. torr pressure. What volume will it occupy at 800. torr pressure? _____

2. A sample of carbon dioxide occupies a volume of 3.50 liters at 125 kPa pressure. What pressure would the gas exert if the volume was decreased to 2.00 liters? _____

3. A 2.0 liter container of nitrogen had a pressure of 3.2 atm. What volume would be necessary to decrease the pressure to 1.0 atm? _____

4. Ammonia gas occupies a volume of 450. mL at a pressure of 720. mm Hg. What volume will it occupy at standard pressure? _____

5. A 175 mL sample of neon had its pressure changed from 75 kPa to 150 kPa. What is its new volume? _____

6. A sample of hydrogen at 1.5 atm had its pressure decreased to 0.50 atm producing a new volume of 750 mL. What was its original volume? _____

7. Chlorine gas occupies a volume of 1.2 liters at 720 torr pressure. What volume will it occupy at 1 atm pressure?

_____

8. Fluorine gas exerts a pressure of 900. torr. When the pressure is changed to 1.50 atm, its volume is 250. mL. What was the original volume? _____

Charles' Law

Charles' Law states that the volume of a gas varies directly with the Kelvin temperature, assuming that pressure is constant. We use the following formulas:

$$\frac{V_1}{T_1} = \frac{V_2}{T_2} \quad \text{or} \quad V_1 \times T_2 = V_2 \times T_1$$

$$K = \text{°C} + 273$$

Solve the following problems assuming a constant pressure.

1. A sample of nitrogen occupies a volume of 250 mL at 25° C. What volume will it occupy at 95° C? _____

2. Oxygen gas is at a temperature of 40° C when it occupies a volume of 2.3 liters. To what temperature should it be raised to occupy a volume of 6.5 liters? _____

3. Hydrogen gas was cooled from $1\overline{5}0$° C to $5\overline{0}$° C. Its new volume is 75 mL. What was its original volume?

    _____

4. Chlorine gas occupies a volume of 25 mL at $3\overline{0}0$ K. What volume will it occupy at 600 K? _____

5. A sample of neon gas at $5\overline{0}$° C and a volume of 2.5 liters is cooled to 25° C. What is the new volume? _____

6. Fluorine gas at $30\overline{0}$ K occupies a volume of $50\overline{0}$ mL. To what temperature should it be lowered to bring the volume to $30\overline{0}$ mL? _____

7. Helium occupies a volume of 3.8 liters at -45° C. What volume will it occupy at 45° C? _____

8. A sample of argon gas is cooled and its volume went from $38\overline{0}$ mL to $25\overline{0}$ mL. If its final temperature was -55° C, what was its original temperature? _____

Combined Gas Law

In practical terms, it is often difficult to hold any of the variables constant. When there is a change in pressure, volume and temperature, the combined gas law is used.

$$\frac{P_1 \times V_1}{T_1} = \frac{P_2 \times V_2}{T_2} \quad \text{or} \quad P_1 V_1 T_2 = P_2 V_2 T_1$$

Complete the following chart.

	P_1	V_1	T_1	P_2	V_2	T_2
1	1.5 atm	3.0 L	$2\bar{0}°$ C	2.5 atm		$3\bar{0}°$ C
2	720 torr	256 mL	25° C		250 mL	50° C
3	$6\bar{0}0$ mmHg	2.5 L	22° C	760 mmHg	1.8 L	
4		750 mL	0.0° C	2.0 atm	$5\bar{0}0$ mL	25° C
5	95 kPa	4.0 L		101 kPa	6.0 L	471 K or 198° C
6	650. torr		$10\bar{0}°$ C	900. torr	225 mL	$15\bar{0}°$ C
7	850 mmHg	1.5 L	15° C		2.5 L	$3\bar{0}°$ C
8	125 kPa	125 mL		$10\bar{0}$ kPa	$10\bar{0}$ mL	75° C

Dalton's Law of Partial Pressures

Dalton's Law says that the sum of the individual pressures of all the gases that make up a mixture is equal to the total pressure or: $P_T = P_1 + P_2 + P_3 + \ldots$ The partial pressure of each gas is equal to the mole fraction of each gas x total pressure.

$$P_T = P_1 + P_2 + P_3 + \ldots \quad \text{or} \quad \frac{\text{moles gas}_x}{\text{total moles}} \times P_T = P_x$$

Solve the following problems.

1. A 250. mL sample of oxygen is collected over water at 25° C and 760.0 torr pressure. What is the pressure of the dry gas alone? (Vapor pressure of water at 25° C = 23.8 torr)

   _____

2. A 32.0 mL sample of hydrogen is collected over water at 20° C and 750.0 torr pressure. What is the volume of the dry gas at STP? (Vapor pressure of water at 20° C = 17.5 torr)

   _____

3. A 54.0 mL sample of oxygen is collected over water at 23° C and 770.0 torr pressure. What is the volume of the dry gas at STP? (Vapor pressure of water at 23° C = 21.1 torr)

   _____

4. A mixture of 2.00 moles of H_2, 3.00 moles of NH_3, 4.00 moles of CO_2 and 5.00 moles of N_2 exerts a total pressure of 800 torr. What is the partial pressure of each gas?

   _____

5. The partial pressure of F_2 in a mixture of gases where the total pressure is 1.00 atm is 300. torr. What is the mole fraction of F_2?

   _____

Ideal Gas Law

Use the Ideal Gas Law below to solve the following problems.

$PV = nRT$ where P = pressure in atmospheres
V = volume in liters
n = number of moles of gas
R = Universal Gas Constant
0.0821 L•atm/mol•K
T = Kelvin temperature

1. How many moles of oxygen will occupy a volume of 2.5 liters at 1.2 atm and 25° C? _____

2. What volume will 2.0 moles of nitrogen occupy at 720 torr and 2$\bar{0}$° C? _____

3. What pressure will be exerted by 25 g of CO_2 at a temperature of 25° C and a volume of 50$\bar{0}$ mL?

   _____

4. At what temperature will 5.00 g of Cl_2 exert a pressure of 900. torr at a volume of 75$\bar{0}$ mL? _____

5. What is the density of NH_3 at 80$\bar{0}$ torr and 25° C?

   _____

6. If the density of a gas is 1.2 g/L at 745. torr and 2$\bar{0}$° C, what is its molecular mass? _____

7. How many moles of nitrogen gas will occupy a volume of 347 mL at 6680 torr and 27° C? _____

8. What volume will 454 grams (1 lb) of hydrogen occupy at 1.05 atm and 25° C? _____

9. Find the number of grams of CO_2 that exert a pressure of 785 torrs at a volume of 32.5 L and a temperature of 32° C.

   _____

Element Symbols

An element symbol can stand for one atom of the element or one mole of atoms of the element.
(One mole = 6.02×10^{23} atoms of an element.)
Write the symbol for the following elements.

1. oxygen _____
2. hydrogen _____
3. chlorine _____
4. mercury _____
5. fluorine _____
6. barium _____
7. helium _____
8. uranium _____
9. radon _____
10. sulfur _____

11. plutonium _____
12. americium _____
13. radium _____
14. germanium _____
15. zinc _____
16. arsenic _____
17. lead _____
18. iron _____
19. calcium _____
20. cobalt _____

Write the name of the element that corresponds to each of the following symbols.

21. Kr _____
22. K _____
23. C _____
24. Ne _____
25. Si _____
26. Zr _____
27. Sn _____
28. Pt _____
29. Na _____
30. Al _____

31. Cu _____
32. Ag _____
33. P _____
34. Mn _____
35. I _____
36. Au _____
37. Mg _____
38. Ni _____
39. Br _____
40. Hg _____

Atomic Structure

An atom is made up of protons and neutrons (both found in the nucleus) and electrons (in the surrounding electron cloud). The atomic number is equal to the number of protons. The mass number is equal to the number of protons plus neutrons. In a neutral atom, the number of protons equals the number of electrons. The charge on an ion indicates an imbalance between protons and electrons. Too many electrons produces a negative charge, too few, a positive charge.

This structure can be written as part of a chemical symbol.

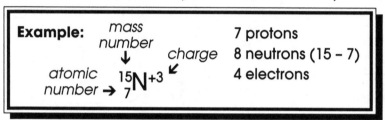

Example: $mass$ $number$ ↓ $atomic$ $number$ → $^{15}_{7}N^{+3}$ ← $charge$

7 protons
8 neutrons (15 – 7)
4 electrons

Complete the following chart.

Element/ Ion	Atomic Number	Atomic Mass	Mass Number	Protons	Neutrons	Electrons
1. H						
2. H⁺						
3. $^{12}_{6}C$						
4. $^{7}_{3}Li^{+}$						
5. $^{35}_{17}Cl^{-}$						
6. $^{39}_{19}K$						
7. $^{24}_{12}Mg^{2+}$						
8. As³⁻						
9. Ag						
10. Ag⁺¹						
11. S⁻²						
12. U						

Isotopes and Average Atomic Mass

Elements come in a variety of isotopes, meaning they are made up of atoms with the same atomic number but different atomic masses. These atoms differ in the number of neutrons.

The average atomic mass is the weighted average of all the isotopes of an element.

Example: A sample of cesium is 75% ^{133}Cs, 20% ^{132}Cs and 5% ^{134}Cs. What is its average atomic mass?

Answer:
.75 x 133 =   99.75
.20 x 132 =   26.4
.05 = 134 =   6.7
Total = 132.85 amu = average atomic mass

Determine the average atomic mass of the following mixtures of isotopes.

1. 80% ^{127}I, 17% ^{126}I, 3% ^{128}I

    _____

2. 50% ^{197}Au, 50% ^{198}Au

    _____

3. 15% ^{55}Fe, 85% ^{56}Fe

    _____

4. 99% ^{1}H, 0.8% ^{2}H, 0.2% ^{3}H

    _____

5. 95% ^{14}N, 3% ^{15}N, 2% ^{16}N

    _____

6. 98% ^{12}C, 2% ^{14}C

    _____

Electron Configuration

Electrons are distributed in the electron cloud into principal energy levels (1, 2, 3, ...), sublevels (s, p, d, f), orbitals (s has 1, p has 3, d has 5, f has 7) and spin (two electrons allowed per orbital).

Example: Draw the electron configuration of sodium (atomic #11).

Answer: $1s^2$ $2s^2$ $2p^6$ $3s^1$

↑↓ ↑↓   ↑↓ ↑↓ ↑↓   ↑

Draw the electron configurations of the following atoms.

1. Cl

2. N

3. Al

4. O

Valence Electrons

The valence electrons are the electrons in the outermost principal energy level. They are always "s" or "s and p" electrons. Since the total number of electrons possible in s and p sublevels is eight, there can be no more than eight valence electrons.

Determine the number of valence electrons in the atoms below.

Example: carbon
Electron configuration is $1s^2$ $\boxed{2s^2 \; 2p^2}$.
Carbon has 4 valence electrons.

1. fluorine _____

2. phosphorus _____

3. calcium _____

4. nitrogen _____

5. iron _____

6. argon _____

7. potassium _____

8. helium _____

9. magnesium _____

10. sulfur _____

11. lithium _____

12. zinc _____

13. carbon _____

14. iodine _____

15. oxygen _____

16. barium _____

17. aluminum _____

18. hydrogen _____

19. xenon _____

20. copper _____

Nuclear Decay

Predict the products of the following nuclear reactions.

1. $^{42}K \rightarrow {}_{-1}^{0}e \ +$ _____

2. $^{239}Pu \rightarrow {}_{2}^{4}He \ +$ _____

3. $^{235}_{92}U \rightarrow$ _____ $+ \ ^{231}_{90}Th$

4. $^{1}_{1}H \ + \ ^{3}_{1}H \rightarrow$ _____

5. $^{6}_{3}Li \ + \ ^{1}_{0}n \rightarrow {}_{2}^{4}He \ +$ _____

6. $^{27}_{13}Al \ + \ ^{4}_{2}He \rightarrow {}_{15}^{30}P \ +$ _____

7. $^{9}_{4}Be \ + \ ^{1}_{1}H \rightarrow$ _____ $+ \ ^{4}_{2}He$

8. $^{37}K \rightarrow {}_{+1}^{0}e \ +$ _____

9. _____ $+ \ ^{1}_{0}n \rightarrow {}_{56}^{142}Ba \ + \ ^{91}_{36}Kr \ + \ 3^{1}_{0}n$

10. $^{238}_{92}U \ + \ ^{4}_{2}He \rightarrow$ _____ $+ \ ^{1}_{0}n$

Half-Life of Radioactive Isotopes

1. How much of a 100.0 g sample of ^{198}Au is left after 8.10 days if its half-life is 2.70 days?

   _____

2. A 50.0 g sample of ^{16}N decays to 12.5 g in 14.4 seconds. What is its half-life?

   _____

3. The half-life of ^{42}K is 12.4 hours. How much of a $75\bar{0}$ g sample is left after 62.0 hours?

   _____

4. What is the half-life of ^{99}Tc if a $50\bar{0}$ g sample decays to 62.5 g in 639,000 years?

   _____

5. The half-life of ^{232}Th is 1.4×10^{10} years. If there are 25.0 g of the sample left after 2.8×10^{10} years, how many grams were in the original sample?

   _____

6. There are 5.0 g of ^{131}I left after 40.35 days. How many grams were in the original sample if its half-life is 8.07 days?

   _____

Periodic Table Worksheet

1. Where are the most active metals located? _____

   _____

2. Where are the most active nonmetals located?_____

   _____

3. As you go from left to right across a period, the atomic size (decreases / increases). Why? _____

   _____

4. As you travel down a group, the atomic size (decreases / increases). Why? _____

   _____

5. A negative ion is (larger / smaller) than its parent atom.

6. A positive ion is (larger / smaller) than its parent atom.

7. As you go from left to right across a period, the first ionization energy generally (decreases / increases). Why?

   _____

   _____

8. As you go down a group, the first ionization energy generally (decreases / increases). Why?_____

   _____

   _____

9. Where is the highest electronegativity found?_____

10. Where is the lowest electronegativity found? _____

11. Elements of Group 1 are called _____ .

Periodic Table Worksheet continued

12. Elements of Group 2 are called _____

    _____ .

13. Elements of Group 3-12 are called_____ .

14. As you go from left to right across the periodic table, the elements go from (metals / nonmetals) to (metals / nonmetals).

15. Group 17 elements are called_____ .

16. The most active element in Group 17 is _____ .

17. Group 18 elements are called_____ .

18. What sublevels are filling across the Transition Elements?

    _____

19. Elements within a group have a similar number of

    _____ .

20. Elements across a series have the same number of

    _____ .

21. A colored ion generally indicates a_____ .

22. As you go down a group, the elements generally become (more / less) metallic.

23. The majority of elements in the periodic table are (metals / nonmetals).

24. Elements in the periodic table are arranged according to their _____ .

25. An element with both metallic and nonmetallic properties is called a _____ .

Ionic Bonding

Ionic bonding occurs when a metal transfers one or more electrons to a nonmetal in an effort to attain a stable octet of electrons. For example, the transfer of an electron from sodium to chlorine can be depicted by a Lewis dot diagram.

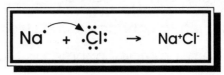

Calcium would need two chlorine atoms to get rid of its two valence electrons.

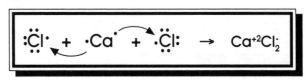

Show the transfer of electrons in the following combinations.

1. K + F

2. Mg + I

3. Be + S

4. Na + O

5. Al + Br

Covalent Bonding

Covalent bonding occurs when two or more nonmetals share electrons, attempting to attain a stable octet of electrons at least part of the time. For example:

Note that hydrogen is content with 2, not 8, electrons.

Show how covalent bonding occurs in each of the following pairs of atoms. Atoms may share one, two or three pairs of electrons.

1. H + H (H_2)

2. F + F (F_2)

3. O + O (O_2)

4. N + N (N_2)

5. C + O (CO_2)

6. H + O (H_2O)

Shapes of Molecules

Using VSEPR Theory, name and sketch the shape of the following molecules.

1. N_2

2. H_2O

3. CO_2

4. NH_3

5. CH_4

6. SO_3

7. HF

8. CH_3OH

9. H_2S

10. I_2

11. $CHCl_3$

12. O_2

Polarity of Molecules

Determine whether the following molecules are polar or nonpolar.

1. N_2

2. H_2O

3. CO_2

4. NH_3

5. CH_4

6. SO_3

7. HF

8. CH_3OH

9. H_2S

10. I_2

11. $CHCl_3$

12. O_2

Writing Formulas (Criss-Cross Method)

Write the formulas of the compounds produced from the listed ions.

	Cl^-	CO_3^{-2}	OH^-	SO_4^{-2}	PO_4^{-3}	NO_3^-
1. Na^+						
2. NH_4^+						
3. K^+						
4. Ca^{+2}						
5. Mg^{+2}						
6. Zn^{+2}						
7. Fe^{+3}						
8. Al^{+3}						
9. Co^{+3}						
10. Fe^{+2}						
11. H^+						

Naming Ionic Compounds

Name the following compounds using the Stock Naming System.

1. $CaCO_3$ _____

2. KCl _____

3. $FeSO_4$ _____

4. $LiBr$ _____

5. $MgCl_2$ _____

6. $FeCl_3$ _____

7. $Zn_3(PO_4)_2$ _____

8. NH_4NO_3 _____

9. $Al(OH)_3$ _____

10. $CuC_2H_3O_2$ _____

11. $PbSO_3$ _____

12. $NaClO_3$ _____

13. CaC_2O_4 _____

14. Fe_2O_3 _____

15. $(NH_4)_3PO_4$ _____

16. $NaHSO_4$ _____

17. Hg_2Cl_2 _____

18. $Mg(NO_2)_2$ _____

19. $CuSO_4$ _____

20. $NaHCO_3$ _____

21. $NiBr_3$ _____

22. $Be(NO_3)_2$ _____

23. $ZnSO_4$ _____

24. $AuCl_3$ _____

25. $KMnO_4$ _____

Naming Molecular Compounds

Name the following covalent compounds.

1. CO_2 _____

2. CO _____

3. SO_2 _____

4. SO_3 _____

5. N_2O _____

6. NO _____

7. N_2O_3 _____

8. NO_2 _____

9. N_2O_4 _____

10. N_2O_5 _____

11. PCl_3 _____

12. PCl_5 _____

13. NH_3 _____

14. SCl_6 _____

15. P_2O_5 _____

16. CCl_4 _____

17. SiO_2 _____

18. CS_2 _____

19. OF_2 _____

20. PBr_3 _____

Naming Acids

Name the following acids.

1. HNO_3 _____

2. HCl _____

3. H_2SO_4 _____

4. H_2SO_3 _____

5. $HC_2H_3O_2$ _____

6. HBr _____

7. HNO_2 _____

8. H_3PO_4 _____

9. H_2S _____

10. H_2CO_3 _____

Write the formulas of the following acids.

11. sulfuric acid _____

12. nitric acid _____

13. hydrochloric acid _____

14. acetic acid _____

15. hydrofluoric acid _____

16. phosphorous acid _____

17. carbonic acid _____

18. nitrous acid _____

19. phosphoric acid _____

20. hydrosulfuric acid _____

Writing Formulas From Names

Write the formulas of the following compounds.

1. ammonium phosphate   _____

2. iron (II) oxide   _____

3. iron (III) oxide   _____

4. carbon monoxide   _____

5. calcium chloride   _____

6. potassium nitrate   _____

7. magnesium hydroxide   _____

8. aluminum sulfate   _____

9. copper (II) sulfate   _____

10. lead (IV) chromate   _____

11. diphosphorus pentoxide   _____

12. potassium permanganate   _____

13. sodium hydrogen carbonate   _____

14. zinc nitrate   _____

15. aluminum sulfite   _____

Gram Formula Mass

Determine the gram formula mass (the mass of one mole) of each compound below.

1. $KMnO_4$ _____

2. KCl _____

3. Na_2SO_4 _____

4. $Ca(NO_3)_2$ _____

5. $Al_2(SO_4)_3$ _____

6. $(NH_4)_3PO_4$ _____

7. $CuSO_4 \bullet 5H_2O$ _____

8. $Mg_3(PO_4)_2$ _____

9. $Zn(C_2H_3O_2)_2 \bullet 2H_2O$ _____

10. $Zn_3(PO_4)_2 \bullet 4H_2O$ _____

11. H_2CO_3 _____

12. $Hg_2Cr_2O_7$ _____

13. $Ba(ClO_3)_2$ _____

14. $Fe_2(SO_3)_3$ _____

15. $NH_4C_2H_3O_2$ _____

Moles and Mass

Determine the number of moles in each of the quantities below.

1. 25 g of NaCl

_____

2. 125 g of H_2SO_4

_____

3. 100. g of $KMnO_4$

_____

4. 74 g of KCl

_____

5. 35 g of $CuSO_4 \bullet 5H_2O$

_____

Determine the number of grams in each of the quantities below.

6. 2.5 moles of NaCl

_____

7. 0.50 moles of H_2SO_4

_____

8. 1.70 moles of $KMnO_4$

_____

9. 0.25 moles of KCl

_____

10. 3.2 moles of $CuSO_4 \bullet 5H_2O$

_____

The Mole and Volume

For gases at STP (273 K and 1 atm pressure), one mole occupies a volume of 22.4 L. What volume will the following quantities of gases occupy at STP?

1. 1.00 mole of H_2

   _____

2. 3.20 moles of O_2

   _____

3. 0.750 mole of N_2

   _____

4. 1.75 moles of CO_2

   _____

5. 0.50 mole of NH_3

   _____

6. 5.0 g of H_2

   _____

7. 100. g of O_2

   _____

8. 28.0 g of N_2

   _____

9. 60. g of CO_2

   _____

10. 10. g of NH_3

    _____

The Mole and Avogadro's Number

> One mole of a substance contains Avogadro's Number (6.02×10^{23}) of molecules.

How many molecules are in the quantities below?

1. 2.0 moles

   _____

2. 1.5 moles

   _____

3. 0.75 mole

   _____

4. 15 moles

   _____

5. 0.35 mole

   _____

How many moles are in the number of molecules below?

6. 6.02×10^{23}

   _____

7. 1.204×10^{24}

   _____

8. 1.5×10^{20}

   _____

9. 3.4×10^{26}

   _____

10. 7.5×10^{19}

   _____

Mixed Mole Problems

Solve the following problems.

1. How many grams are there in 1.5×10^{25} molecules of CO_2?

   _____

2. What volume would the CO_2 in Problem 1 occupy at STP?

   _____

3. A sample of NH_3 gas occupies 75.0 liters at STP. How many molecules is this?

   _____

4. What is the mass of the sample of NH_3 in Problem 3?

   _____

5. How many atoms are there in 1.3×10^{22} molecules of NO_2?

   _____

6. A 5.0 g sample of O_2 is in a container at STP. What volume is the container?

   _____

7. How many molecules of O_2 are in the container in Problem 6? How many atoms of oxygen?

   _____

   _____

Percentage Composition

Determine the percentage composition of each of the compounds below.

1. $KMnO_4$

   K = _____

   Mn = _____

   O = _____

2. HCl

   H = _____

   Cl = _____

3. $Mg(NO_3)_2$

   Mg = _____

   N = _____

   O = _____

4. $(NH_4)_3PO_4$

   N = _____

   H = _____

   P = _____

   O = _____

5. $Al_2(SO_4)_3$

   Al = _____

   S = _____

   O = _____

Solve the following problems.

6. How many grams of oxygen can be produced from the decomposition of 100. g of $KClO_3$? _____

7. How much iron can be recovered from 25.0 g of Fe_2O_3?

   _____

8. How much silver can be produced from 125 g of Ag_2S?

   _____

Determining Empirical Formulas

What is the empirical formula (lowest whole number ratio) of the compounds below?

1. 75% carbon, 25% hydrogen

   _____

2. 52.7% potassium, 47.3% chlorine

   _____

3. 22.1% aluminum, 25.4% phosphorus, 52.5% oxygen

   _____

4. 13% magnesium, 87% bromine

   _____

5. 32.4% sodium, 22.5% sulfur, 45.1% oxygen

   _____

6. 25.3% copper, 12.9% sulfur, 25.7% oxygen, 36.1% water

   _____

Determining Molecular Formulas (True Formulas)

Solve the problems below.

1. The empirical formula of a compound is NO_2. Its molecular mass is 92 g/mol. What is its molecular formula?

    _____

2. The empirical formula of a compound is CH_2. Its molecular mass is 70 g/mol. What is its molecular formula?

    _____

3. A compound is found to be 40.0% carbon, 6.7% hydrogen and 53.5% oxygen. Its molecular mass is 60. g/mol. What is its molecular formula?

    _____

4. A compound is 64.9% carbon, 13.5% hydrogen and 21.6% oxygen. Its molecular mass is 74 g/mol. What is its molecular formula?

    _____

5. A compound is 54.5% carbon, 9.1% hydrogen and 36.4% oxygen. Its molecular mass is 88 g/mol. What is its molecular formula?

    _____

Composition of Hydrates

A hydrate is an ionic compound with water molecules loosely bonded to its crystal structure. The water is in a specific ratio to each formula unit of the salt. For example, the formula $CuSO_4 \cdot 5H_2O$ indicates that there are five water molecules for every one formula unit of $CuSO_4$.

Answer the questions below.

1. What percentage of water is found in $CuSO_4 \cdot 5H_2O$?

   _____

2. What percentage of water is found in $Na_2S \cdot 9H_2O$?

   _____

3. A 5.0 g sample of a hydrate of $BaCl_2$ was heated, and only 4.3 g of the anhydrous salt remained. What percentage of water was in the hydrate?

   _____

4. A 2.5 g sample of a hydrate of $Ca(NO_3)_2$ was heated, and only 1.7 g of the anhydrous salt remained. What percentage of water was in the hydrate?

   _____

5. A 3.0 g sample of $Na_2CO_3 \cdot H_2O$ is heated to constant mass. How much anhydrous salt remains?

   _____

6. A 5.0 g sample of $Cu(NO_3)_2 \cdot nH_2O$ is heated, and 3.9 g of the anhydrous salt remains. What is the value of n?

   _____

Balancing Chemical Equations

Rewrite and balance the equations below.

1. $N_2 + H_2 \rightarrow NH_3$ _____

2. $KClO_3 \rightarrow KCl + O_2$ _____

3. $NaCl + F_2 \rightarrow NaF + Cl_2$ _____

4. $H_2 + O_2 \rightarrow H_2O$ _____

5. $AgNO_3 + MgCl_2 \rightarrow AgCl + Mg(NO_3)_2$ _____

6. $AlBr_3 + K_2SO_4 \rightarrow KBr + Al_2(SO_4)_3$ _____

7. $CH_4 + O_2 \rightarrow CO_2 + H_2O$ _____

8. $C_3H_8 + O_2 \rightarrow CO_2 + H_2O$ _____

9. $C_8H_{18} + O_2 \rightarrow 1O_2 + H_2O$ _____

10. $FeCl_3 + NaOH \rightarrow Fe(OH)_3 + NaCl$ _____

11. $P + O_2 \rightarrow P_2O_5$ _____

12. $Na + H_2O \rightarrow NaOH + H_2$ _____

13. $Ag_2O \rightarrow Ag + O_2$ _____

14. $S_8 + O_2 \rightarrow SO_3$ _____

15. $CO_2 + H_2O \rightarrow C_6H_{12}O_6 + O_2$ _____

16. $K + MgBr_2 \rightarrow KBr + Mg$ _____

17. $HCl + CaCO_3 \rightarrow CaCl_2 + H_2O + CO_2$ _____

Word Equations

Write the word equations below as chemical equations and balance.

1. zinc + lead (II) nitrate yield zinc nitrate + lead

2. aluminum bromide + chlorine yield
   aluminum chloride + bromine

3. sodium phosphate + calcium chloride yield
   calcium phosphate + sodium chloride

4. potassium chlorate when heated yields potassium
   chloride + oxygen gas

5. aluminum + hydrochloric acid yield
   aluminum chloride + hydrogen gas

6. calcium hydroxide + phosphoric acid yield
   calcium phosphate + water

7. copper + sulfuric acid yield copper (II) sulfate + water +
   sulfur dioxide

8. hydrogen + nitrogen monoxide yield water + nitrogen

Classification of Chemical Reactions

Classify the reactions below as synthesis, decomposition, single replacement (cationic or anionic) or double replacement.

1. $2H_2 + O_2 \rightarrow 2H_2O$

_____

2. $2H_2O \rightarrow 2H_2 + O_2$

_____

3. $Zn + H_2SO_4 \rightarrow ZnSO_4 + H_2$

_____

4. $2CO + O_2 \rightarrow 2CO_2$

_____

5. $2HgO \rightarrow 2Hg + O_2$

_____

6. $2KBr + Cl_2 \rightarrow 2KCl + Br_2$

_____

7. $CaO + H_2O \rightarrow Ca(OH)_2$

_____

8. $AgNO_3 + NaCl \rightarrow AgCl + NaNO_3$

_____

9. $2H_2O_2 \rightarrow 2H_2O + O_2$

_____

10. $Ca(OH)_2 + H_2SO_4 \rightarrow CaSO_4 + 2H_2O$

_____

Predicting Products of Chemical Reactions

Predict the products of the reactions below. Then, write the balanced equation and classify the reaction.

1. magnesium bromide + chlorine

2. aluminum + iron (III) oxide

3. silver nitrate + zinc chloride

4. hydrogen peroxide (catalyzed by manganese dioxide)

5. zinc + hydrochloric acid

6. sulfuric acid + sodium hydroxide

7. sodium + hydrogen

8. acetic acid + copper

Stoichiometry: Mole-Mole Problems

1. $N_2 + 3H_2 \rightarrow 2NH_3$

   How many moles of hydrogen are needed to completely react with two moles of nitrogen?

   _____

2. $2KClO_3 \rightarrow 2KCl + 3O_2$

   How many moles of oxygen are produced by the decomposition of six moles of potassium chlorate?

   _____

3. $Zn + 2HCl \rightarrow ZnCl_2 + H_2$

   How many moles of hydrogen are produced from the reaction of three moles of zinc with an excess of hydrochloric acid?

   _____

4. $C_3H_8 + 5O_2 \rightarrow 3CO_2 + 4H_2O$

   How many moles of oxygen are necessary to react completely with four moles of propane (C_3H_8)?

   _____

5. $K_3PO_4 + Al(NO_3)_3 \rightarrow 3KNO_3 + AlPO_4$

   How many moles of potassium nitrate are produced when two moles of potassium phosphate react with two moles of aluminum nitrate?

   _____

Stoichiometry: Volume-Volume Problems

1. $N_2 + 3H_2 \rightarrow 2NH_3$

   What volume of hydrogen is necessary to react with five liters of nitrogen to produce ammonia? (Assume constant temperature and pressure.)

   _____

2. What volume of ammonia is produced in the reaction in Problem 1?

   _____

3. $C_3H_8 + 5O_2 \rightarrow 3CO_2 + 4H_2O$

   If 20 liters of oxygen are consumed in the above reaction, how many liters of carbon dioxide are produced?

   _____

4. $2H_2O \rightarrow 2H_2 + O_2$

   If 30 mL of hydrogen are produced in the above reaction, how many milliliters of oxygen are produced?

   _____

5. $2CO + O_2 \rightarrow 2CO_2$

   How many liters of carbon dioxide are produced if 75 liters of carbon monoxide are burned in oxygen? How many liters of oxygen are necessary?

   _____

   _____

Stoichiometry: Mass-Mass Problems

1. $2KClO_3 \rightarrow 2KCl + 3O_2$

   How many grams of potassium chloride are produced if 25 g of potassium chlorate decompose?

   _____

2. $N_2 + 3H_2 \rightarrow 2NH_3$

   How many grams of hydrogen are necessary to react completely with 50.0 g of nitrogen in the above reaction?

   _____

3. How many grams of ammonia are produced in the reaction in Problem 2?

   _____

4. $2AgNO_3 + BaCl_2 \rightarrow 2AgCl + Ba(NO_3)_2$

   How many grams of silver chloride are produced from 5.0 g of silver nitrate reacting with an excess of barium chloride?

   _____

5. How much barium chloride is necessary to react with the silver nitrate in Problem 4?

   _____

Stoichiometry: Mixed Problems

1. $N_2 + 3H_2 \rightarrow 2NH_3$

    What volume of NH_3 at STP is produced if 25.0 g of N_2 is reacted with an excess of H_2?

    _____

2. $2KClO_3 \rightarrow 2KCl + 3O_2$

    If 5.0 g of $KClO_3$ is decomposed, what volume of O_2 is produced at STP?

    _____

3. How many grams of KCl are produced in Problem 2?

    _____

4. $Zn + 2HCl \rightarrow ZnCl_2 + H_2$

    What volume of hydrogen at STP is produced when 2.5 g of zinc react with an excess of hydrochloric acid?

    _____

5. $H_2SO_4 + 2NaOH \rightarrow H_2O + Na_2SO_4$

    How many molecules of water are produced if 2.0 g of sodium sulfate are produced in the above reaction?

    _____

6. $2AlCl_3 \rightarrow 2Al + 3Cl_2$

    If 10.0 g of aluminum chloride are decomposed, how many molecules of Cl_2 are produced?

    _____

Stoichiometry: Limiting Reagent

1. $N_2 + 3H_2 \rightarrow 2NH_3$

    How many grams of NH_3 can be produced from the reaction of 28 g of N_2 and 25 g of H_2?

    _____

2. How much of the excess reagent in Problem 1 is left over?

    _____

3. $Mg + 2HCl \rightarrow MgCl_2 + H_2$

    What volume of hydrogen at STP is produced from the reaction of 50.0 g of Mg and the equivalent of 75 g of HCl?

    _____

4. How much of the excess reagent in Problem 3 is left over?

    _____

5. $3AgNO_3 + Na_3PO_4 \rightarrow Ag_3PO_4 + 3NaNO_3$

    Silver nitrate and sodium phosphate are reacted in equal amounts of 200. g each. How many grams of silver phosphate are produced?

    _____

6. How much of the excess reagent in Problem 5 is left?

    _____

Solubility Curves

Answer the following questions based on the solubility curve below.

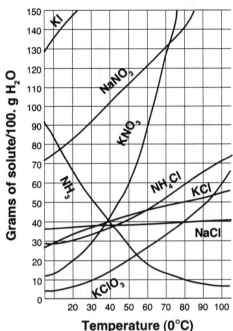

1. Which salt is least soluble in water at 20° C?

    _____

2. How many grams of potassium chloride can be dissolved in 200 g of water at 80° C? _____

3. At 40° C, how much potassium nitrate can be dissolved in 300 g of water? _____

4. Which salt shows the least change in solubility from 0° – 100° C? _____

5. At 30° C, 90 g of sodium nitrate is dissolved in 100 g of water. Is this solution saturated, unsaturated or supersaturated? _____

6. A saturated solution of potassium chlorate is formed from one hundred grams of water. If the saturated solution is cooled from 80° C to 50° C, how many grams of precipitate are formed? _____

7. What compound shows a decrease in solubility from 0° to 100° C? _____

8. Which salt is most soluble at 10° C? _____

9. Which salt is least soluble at 50° C? _____

10. Which salt is least soluble at 90° C? _____

Molarity (M)

$$\text{Molarity} = \frac{\text{moles of solute}}{\text{liter of solution}}$$

Solve the problems below.

1. What is the molarity of a solution in which 58 g of NaCl are dissolved in 1.0 L of solution?

   _____

2. What is the molarity of a solution in which 10.0 g of $AgNO_3$ is dissolved in 500. mL of solution?

   _____

3. How many grams of KNO_3 should be used to prepare 2.00 L of a 0.500 M solution?

   _____

4. To what volume should 5.0 g of KCl be diluted in order to prepare a 0.25 M solution?

   _____

5. How many grams of $CuSO_4 \cdot 5H_2O$ are needed to prepare 100. mL of a 0.10 M solution?

   _____

Molality (m)

$$\text{Molality} = \frac{\text{moles of solute}}{\text{Kg of solvent}}$$

Solve the problems below.

1. What is the molality of a solution in which 3.0 moles of NaCl is dissolved in 1.5 Kg of water?

   _____

2. What is the molality of a solution in which 25 g of NaCl is dissolved in 2.0 Kg of water?

   _____

3. What is the molality of a solution in which 15 g of I_2 is dissolved in 500. g of alcohol?

   _____

4. How many grams of I_2 should be added to 750 g of CCl_4 to prepare a 0.020 m solution?

   _____

5. How much water should be added to 5.00 g of KCl to prepare a 0.500 m solution?

   _____

Normality (N)

normality = molarity x total positive oxidation number of solute

Example: What is the normality of 3.0 M of H_2SO_4?

Solution: Since the total positive oxidation number of H_2SO_4 is +2 (2 H^+), N = 6.0.

Solve the problems below.

1. What is the normality of a 2.0 M NaOH solution?

    _____

2. What is the normality of a 2.0 M H_3PO_4 solution?

    _____

3. A solution of H_2SO_4 is 3.0 N. What is its molarity?

    _____

4. What is the normality of a solution in which 2.0 g of $Ca(OH)_2$ is dissolved in 1.0 L of solution?

    _____

5. How much $AlCl_3$ should be dissolved in 2.00 L of solution to produce a 0.150 N solution?

    _____

Electrolytes

Electrolytes are substances that break up (dissociate or ionize) in water to produce ions. These ions are capable of conducting an electric current.

Generally, electrolytes consist of acids, bases and salts (ionic compounds). Nonelectrolytes are usually covalent compounds, with the exception of acids.

Classify the following compounds as either an electrolyte or a nonelectrolyte.

Compound	Electrolyte	Nonelectrolyte
1. NaCl		
2. CH_3OH (methyl alcohol)		
3. $C_3H_5(OH)_3$ (glycerol)		
4. HCl		
5. $C_6H_{12}O_6$ (sugar)		
6. NaOH		
7. C_2H_5OH (ethyl alcohol)		
8. CH_3COOH (acetic acid)		
9. NH_4OH ($NH_3 + H_2O$)		
10. H_2SO_4		

Effect of a Solute on Freezing and Boiling Points

We use the following formulas to calculate changes in freezing and boiling point due to the presence of a nonvolatile solute. Freezing point is always lowered, boiling point is always raised.

$\Delta T_F = m \times d.f. \times k_F$

$\Delta T_B = m \times d.f. \times k_B$

$k_B H_2O = 0.52°\ C/m$

$k_F H_2O = 1.86°\ C/m$

m = molality of solution

k_F and k_B = constants for particular solvent

d.f. = dissociation factor (how many particles solute breaks up into: for a nonelectrolyte, d.f. = 1)

(Theoretical Dissociation Factor is always greater than observed effect.)

Solve the problems below.

1. What is the new boiling point if 25 g of NaCl is dissolved in 1.0 Kg of water?

   _____

2. What is the freezing point of the solution in Problem 1?

   _____

3. What are the new freezing and boiling points of water if 50. g of ethylene glycol (molecular mass = 62 g/mol) is added to 50. g of water?

   _____

4. When 5.0 g of a nonelectrolyte is added to 25 g of water, the new freezing point is -2.5° C. What is the molecular mass of the unknown compound?

   _____

Solubility (Polar vs. Nonpolar)

Generally, "like dissolves like." Polar molecules dissolve other polar molecules and ionic compounds. Nonpolar molecules dissolve other nonpolar molecules. Alcohols, which have characteristics of both, tend to dissolve in both types of solvents, but will not dissolve ionic solids.

Check the appropriate columns as to whether the solute is soluble in a polar or nonpolar solvent.

SOLUTES	SOLVENTS		
	Water	CCl_4	Alcohol
1. NaCl			
2. I_2			
3. ethanol			
4. benzene			
5. Br_2			
6. KNO_3			
7. toluene			
8. $Ca(OH)_2$			

Potential Energy Diagram

Answer the questions using the graph.

1. Is the reaction endothermic or exothermic?

   _____

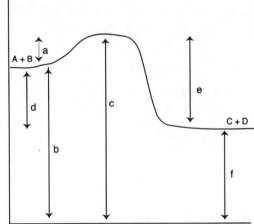

Potential Energy

Reaction Coordinate

A + B ↔ C + D + energy

2. What letter represents the potential energy of the reactants?

   _____

3. What letter represents the potential energy of the products? _____

4. What letter represents the heat of reaction (ΔH)?

   _____

5. What letter represents the activation energy of the forward reaction? _____

6. What letter represents the activation energy of the reverse reaction? _____

7. What letter represents the potential energy of the activated complex? _____

8. Is the reverse reaction endothermic or exothermic?

   _____

9. If a catalyst were added, what letter(s) would change?

   _____

Entropy

Entropy is the degree of randomness in a substance. The symbol for change in entropy is ΔS.

Solids are very ordered and have low entropy. Liquids and aqueous ions have more entropy because they move about more freely, and gases have an even larger amount of entropy. According to the Second Law of Thermodynamics, nature is always proceeding to a state of higher entropy.

Determine whether the following reactions show an increase or decrease in entropy.

1. $2KClO_3(s) \rightarrow 2KCl(s) + 3O_2(g)$ _____

2. $H_2O(l) \rightarrow H_2O(s)$ _____

3. $N_2(g) + 3H_2(g) \rightarrow 2NH_3(g)$ _____

4. $NaCl(s) \rightarrow Na^+(aq) + Cl^-(aq)$ _____

5. $KCl(s) \rightarrow KCl(l)$ _____

6. $CO_2(s) \rightarrow CO_2(g)$ _____

7. $H^+(aq) + C_2H_3O_2^-(aq) \rightarrow HC_2H_3O_3(l)$ _____

8. $C(s) + O_2(g) \rightarrow CO_2(g)$ _____

9. $H_2(g) + Cl_2(g) \rightarrow 2HCl(g)$ _____

10. $Ag^+(aq) + Cl^-(aq) \rightarrow AgCl(s)$ _____

11. $2N_2O_5(g) \rightarrow 4NO_2(g) + O_2(g)$ _____

12. $2Al(s) + 3I_2(s) \rightarrow 2AlI_3(s)$ _____

13. $H^+(aq) + OH^-(aq) \rightarrow H_2O(l)$ _____

14. $2NO(g) \rightarrow N_2(g) + O_2(g)$ _____

15. $H_2O(g) \rightarrow H_2O(l)$ _____

Gibbs Free Energy

For a reaction to be spontaneous, the sign of ΔG (Gibbs Free Energy) must be negative. The mathematical formula for this value is:

$$\Delta G = \Delta H - T\Delta S$$

where ΔH = change in enthalpy or heat of reaction
T = temperature in Kelvin
ΔS = change in entropy or randomness

Answer the questions below.

1. The conditions in which ΔG is always negative is when ΔH is _____ and ΔS is _____ .

2. The conditions in which ΔG is always positive is when ΔH is _____ and ΔS is _____ .

3. When the situation is indeterminate, a low temperature favors the (entropy / enthalpy) factor, and a high temperature favors the (entropy / enthalpy) factor.

Answer Problems 4-6 with always, sometimes or never.

4. The reaction: $Na(OH)_s \rightarrow Na+(aq) + OH^-(aq) + energy$ will _____ be spontaneous.

5. The reaction: $energy + 2H_2(g) + O_2(g) \rightarrow 2H_2O$ (l) will _____ be spontaneous.

6. The reaction: $energy + H_2O(s) \rightarrow H_2O(l)$ will _____ be spontaneous.

7. What is the value of ΔG if $\Delta H = -32.0$ kJ, $\Delta S = +25.0$ kJ/K and T = 293 K? _____

8. Is the reaction in Problem 7 spontaneous? _____

9. What is the value of ΔG if $\Delta H = +12.0$ kJ, $\Delta S = -5.00$ kJ/K and T = 290. K? _____

Equilibrium Constant (K)

Write the expression for the equilibrium constant K for the reactions below.

1. $N_2(g) + 3H_2(g) \leftrightarrow 2NH_3(g)$

2. $2KClO_3(s) \leftrightarrow 2KCl(s) + 3O_2(g)$

3. $H_2O(l) \leftrightarrow H^+(aq) + OH^-(aq)$

4. $2CO(g) + O_2(g) \leftrightarrow 2CO_2(g)$

5. $Li_2CO_3(s) \rightarrow 2Li^+(aq) + CO_3^{-2}(aq)$

Le Chatelier's Principle

Le Chatelier's Principle states that when a system at equilibrium is subjected to a stress, the system will shift its equilibrium point in order to relieve the stress.

Complete the following chart by writing left, right or none for equilibrium shift, and decreases, increases or remains the same for the concentrations of reactants and products, and for the value of K.

$$N_2(g) + 3H_2(g) \leftrightarrow 2NH_3(g) + 22.0 \text{ kcal}$$

Stress	Equilibrium Shift	$[N_2]$	$[H_2]$	$[NH_3]$	K
1. Add N_2	right	____	decreases	increases	remains the same
2. Add H_2			____		
3. Add NH_3				____	
4. Remove N_2		____			
5. Remove H_2			____		
6. Remove NH_3				____	
7. Increase Temperature					
8. Decrease Temperature					
9. Increase Pressure					
10. Decrease Pressure					

Bronsted-Lowry Acids and Bases

According to Bronsted-Lowry theory, an acid is a proton (H+) donor, and a base is a proton acceptor.

$$H^+$$

Example: $HCl + OH^- \rightarrow Cl^- + H_2O$

The HCl acts as an acid, the OH- as a base. This reaction is reversible in that the H_2O can give back the proton to the Cl-.

Label the Bronsted-Lowry acids and bases in the following reactions and show the direction of proton transfer.

$$H^+ \qquad\qquad H^+$$

Example: $H_2O + Cl^- \leftrightarrow OH^- + HCl$

             Acid   Base   Base   Acid

1. $H_2O + H_2O \leftrightarrow H_3O^+ + OH^-$

2. $H_2SO_4^- + OH^- \leftrightarrow HSO_4^- + H_2O$

3. $HSO_4 + H_2O \leftrightarrow SO_4^{-2} + H_3O^+$

4. $OH^- + H_3O^+ \leftrightarrow H_2O + H_2O$

5. $NH_3 + H_2O \leftrightarrow NH_4^+ + OH^-$

Conjugate Acid-Base Pairs

In the exercise, Bronsted-Lowry Acids and Bases, it was shown that after an acid has given up its proton, it is capable of getting back that proton and acting as a base. Conjugate base is what is left after an acid gives up a proton. The stronger the acid, the weaker the conjugate base. The weaker the acid, the stronger the conjugate base.

Fill in the blanks in the table below.

Conjugate Pairs

	ACID	BASE	EQUATION
1.	H_2SO_4	HSO_4^-	$H_2SO_4 \leftrightarrow H^+ + HSO_4^-$
2.	H_3PO_4		
3.		F^-	
4.		NO_3^-	
5.	$H_2PO_4^-$		
6.	H_2O		
7.		SO_4^{-2}	
8.	HPO_4^{-2}		
9.	NH_4^+		
10.		H_2O	

pH and pOH

The pH of a solution indicates how acidic or basic that solution is.

pH range of 0 - 7 acidic

7 neutral

7-14 basic

Since $[H^+][OH^-] = 10^{-14}$ at 25° C, if $[H^+]$ is known, the $[OH^-]$ can be calculated and vice versa.

pH $= -\log [H^+]$ So if $[H^+] = 10^{-6}$ M, pH $= 6$.

pOH $= -\log [OH^-]$ So if $[OH^-] = 10^{-8}$ M, pOH $= 8$.

Together, pH + pOH $= 14$.

Complete the following chart.

	$[H^+]$	pH	$[OH^-]$	pOH	Acidic or Basic
1.	10^{-5} M	5	10^{-9} M	9	Acidic
2.		7			
3.			10^{-4} M		
4.	10^{-2} M				
5.				11	
6.		12			
7.			10^{-5} M		
8.	10^{-11} M				
9.				13	
10.		6			

Acid-Base Titration

To determine the concentration of an acid (or base), we can react it with a base (or acid) of known concentration until it is completely neutralized. This point of exact neutralization, known as the endpoint, is noted by the change in color of the indicator. We use the following equation:

$$N_A \times V_A = N_B \times V_B \qquad \text{where} \quad N = \text{normality}$$
$$V = \text{volume}$$

Solve the problems below.

1. A 25.0 mL sample of HCl was titrated to the endpoint with 15.0 mL of 2.0 N NaOH. What was the normality of the HCl? What was its molarity?

   _____

   _____

2. A 10.0 mL sample of H_2SO_4 was exactly neutralized by 13.5 mL of 1.0 M KOH. What is the molarity of the H_2SO_4? What is the normality?

   _____

   _____

3. How much 1.5 M NaOH is necessary to exactly neutralize 20.0 mL of 2.5 M H_3PO_4?

   _____

4. How much of 0.5 M HNO_3 is necessary to titrate 25.0 mL of 0.05 M $Ca(OH)_2$ solution to the endpoint?

   _____

5. What is the molarity of a NaOH solution if 15.0 mL is exactly neutralized by 7.5 mL of a 0.02 M $HC_2H_3O_2$ solution?

   _____

Hydrolysis of Salts

Salt solutions may be acidic, basic or neutral, depending on the original acid and base that formed the salt.

Strong Acid + Strong Base → Neutral Salt

Strong Acid + Weak Base → Acidic Salt

Weak Acid + Strong Base → Basic Salt

A weak acid and a weak base will produce any type of solution depending on the relative strengths of the acid and base involved.

Complete the table below for each of the following salts.

Salt	Parent Acid	Parent Base	Type of Solution
1. KCl			
2. NH_4NO_3			
3. Na_3PO_4			
4. $CaSO_4$			
5. $AlBr_3$			
6. CuI_2			
7. MgF_2			
8. $NaNO_3$			
9. $LiC_2H_3O_2$			
10. $ZnCl_2$			
11. $SrSO_4$			
12. $Ba_3(PO_4)_2$			

Assigning Oxidation Numbers

Assign oxidation numbers to all of the elements in each of the compounds or ions below.

1. HCl

2. KNO_3

3. OH^-

4. Mg_3N_2

5. $KClO_3$

6. $Al(NO_3)_3$

7. S_8

8. H_2O_2

9. PbO_2

10. $NaHSO_4$

11. H_2SO_3

12. H_2SO_4

13. BaO_2

14. $KMnO_4$

15. LiH

16. MnO_2

17. OF_2

18. SO_3

19. NH_3

20. Na

Redox Reactions

For the equations below, identify the substance oxidized, the substance reduced, the oxidizing agent, the reducing agent, and write the oxidation and reduction half reactions.

> **Example:**
>
>   oxidized reduced
>
> Mg + Br_2 → $MgBr_2$
>
>   reducing oxidizing
>   agent   agent
>
> oxidation half reaction: $Mg° → Mg^{+2} + 2e^-$
>
> reduction half reaction: $2e^- + Br_2° → 2Br^-$

1. $2H_2 + O_2 → 2H_2O$

2. $Fe + Zn^{2+} → Fe^{2+} + Zn$

3. $2Al + 3Fe^{+2} → 2Al^{+3} + 3Fe$

4. $Cu + 2AgNO_3 → Cu(NO_3)_2 + 2Ag$

Balancing Redox Equations

Balance the equations below using the half-reaction method.

1. $Sn° + Ag^+ \rightarrow Sn^{+2} + Ag°$

2. $Cr° + Pb^{2+} \rightarrow Cr^{+3} + Pb°$

3. $KClO_3 \rightarrow KCl + O_2$

4. $NH_3 + O_2 \rightarrow NO + H_2O$

5. $PbS + H_2O_2 \rightarrow PbSO_4 + H_2O$

6. $H_2S + HNO_3 \rightarrow S + NO + H_2O$

7. $MnO_2 + H_2C_2O_4 + H_2SO_4 \rightarrow MnSO_4 + CO_2 + H_2O$

8. $H_2S + H_2SO_3 \rightarrow S + H_2O$

9. $KIO_3 + H_2SO_3 \rightarrow KI + H_2SO_4$

10. $K_2Cr_2O_7 + HCl \rightarrow KCl + CrCl_3 + Cl_2 + H_2O$

The Electrochemical Cell

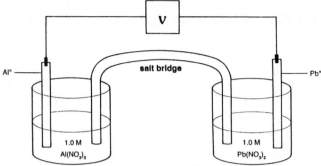

Answer the questions below referring to the above diagram and a Table of Standard Electrode Potentials.

1. Which is more easily oxidized, metal, aluminum or lead? ___

2. What is the balanced equation showing the spontaneous reaction that occurs? _____

3. What is the maximum voltage that the above cell can produce? _____

4. What is the direction of electron flow in the wire? _____

   _____

5. What is the direction of positive ion flow in the salt bridge?

   _____

6. Which electrode is decreasing in size? _____

7. Which electrode is increasing in size? _____

8. What is happening to the concentration of aluminum ions?

   _____

9. What is happening to the concentration of lead ions? ____

10. What is the voltage in this cell when the reaction reaches equilibrium? _____

11. Which is the anode? _____

12. Which is the cathode? _____

13. What is the positive electrode? _____

14. What is the negative electrode? _____

Naming Hydrocarbons

Name the compounds below according to the IUPAC naming system

1.
```
     H   H   H
     |   |   |
H  – C – C – C – H
     |   |   |
     H   H   H
```

5.
```
     H   H     H
     |   |     |
H  – C – C  –  C – H
     |   |     |
     H   H   H–C–H
               |
               H
```

2.
```
     H   H   H   H
     |   |   |   |
H  – C = C – C – C – H
             |   |
             H   H
```

6.
```
     H    CH₃  H
     |    |    |
H  – C  – C  – C – H
     |    |    |
     H    H    H
```

3.
```
                 H
                 |
H – C ≡ C  –  C – H
                 |
                 H
```

7.
```
     H   H   H   H   H
     |   |   |   |   |
H  – C – C = C – C – C – H
                 |   |
                 H   H
```

4.
```
     H   H   H   CH₃  H
     |   |   |   |    |
H  – C – C – C – C  – C – H
     |   |   |   |    |
     H   H   H   H    H
```

8.
```
                    H
                    |
                 H–C–H
                    |
     H   H   H–C–H  H   H
     |   |    |     |   |
H  – C – C  – C  –  C – C – H
     |   |    |     |   |
     H   H  H–C–H   H   H
                |
             H–C–H
                |
                H
```

Structure of Hydrocarbons

Draw the structure of the compounds below.

1. ethane

2. propene

3. 2-butene

4. methane

5. ethyne

6. 3, 3-dimethyl pentane

7. 2, 3-dimethyl pentane

8. n-butyne

Functional Groups

Classify each of the organic compounds below as an alcohol, carboxylic acid, aldehyde, ketone, ether or ester, and draw its structural formula.

1. CH_3COOH

2. CH_3COCH_3

3. CH_3CH_2OH

4. $CH_3CH_2OCH_3$

5. CH_3CH_2CHO

6. $CH_3CH(OH)CH_3$

7. CH_3CH_2COOH

8. $CH_3CH_2COOCH_3$

9. $CH_3CH_2COCH_3$

10. CH_3OCH_3

Naming Other Organic Compounds

Name the compounds below.

1.
```
        H   H
        |   |
  H  –  C – C – OH
        |   |
        H   H
```

6.
```
        H   O           H
        |   ||          |
  H  –  C – C – O  –  C – H
        |               |
        H               H
```

2.
```
        H   O   H
        |   ||  |
  H  –  C – C – C – H
        |       |
        H       H
```

7.
```
        H   OH  H   H
        |   |   |   |
  H  –  C – C – C – C – H
        |   |   |   |
        H   H   H   H
```

3.
```
        H   H   H   O
        |   |   |   ||
  H  –  C – C – C – C – H
        |   |   |
        H   H   H
```

8.
```
        H   H   O
        |   |   ||
  H  –  C – C – C – OH
        |   |
        H   H
```

4.
```
        H   O
        |   ||
  H  –  C – C – OH
        |
        H
```

9.
```
        H   O
        |   ||
  H  –  C – C – H
        |
        H
```

5.
```
        H       H
        |       |
  H  –  C – O – C – H
        |       |
        H       H
```

10.
```
        H   H   O   H
        |   |   ||  |
  H  –  C – C – C – C – H
        |   |       |
        H   H       H
```

Structures of Other Organic Compounds

Draw the structures of the compounds below.

1. butanoic acid

2. methanal

3. methanol

4. butanone

5. diethyl ether

6. methylmethanoate
   (methyl formate)

7. 3-pentanol

8. methanoic acid
   (formic acid)

9. propanal

10. 2-pentanone

2. 1. 5° C; 2. 15° C; 3. 5° C; 4. A; 5. C;
   6. E; 7. B; 8. D; 9. B, D; 10. A, C, E;
   11. D; 12. B

3. 1. 1$\overline{0}$00; 2. 250; 3. 12,000; 4. 46,000;
   5. 5,000; 6. 4$\overline{0}$00

4. 1. 22° C; 2. 52° C; 3. 85° C;
   4. 550 torr; 5. 285 torr; 6. 110 torr;
   7. 43° C; 8. 68° C; 9. 100° C; 10. C

5. 1. element; 2. compound;
   3. heterogeneous;
   4. homogeneous; 5. element;
   6. compound; 7. heterogeneous;
   8. compound; 9. homogeneous;
   10. element

6. 1. physical; 2. physical; 3. chemical;
   4. physical; 5. chemical; 6. chemical;
   7. physical; 8. physical; 9. chemical;
   10. chemical; 11. physical;
   12. physical; 13. chemical;
   14. physical; 15. physical

7. 1. physical; 2. chemical; 3. physical;
   4. physical; 5. chemical; 6. chemical;
   7. chemical; 8. physical; 9. physical;
   10. chemical; 11. physical;
   12. chemical; 13. chemical;
   14. chemical; 15. physical;
   16. chemical; 17. physical

8. 1. 231 mL; 2. 219 kPa; 3. 6.4 L;
   4. 426 mL; 5. 88 mL; 6. 250 mL;
   7. 1.1 L; 8. 317 mL

9. 1. 310 mL; 2. 880 K or 610° C;
   3. 98 mL; 4. 50. mL; 5. 2.3 L; 6. 180 K
   or -93° C; 7. 5.3 L; 8. 331 K or 58° C

10. 1. 1.9 L; 2. 8$\overline{0}$0 torr; 3. -4° C;
    4. 1.2 atm; 5. 22° C; 6. 275 mL;
    7. 540 mmHg; 8. 544 K or 271° C

11. 1. 736. torr; 2. 28.7 mL; 3. 49.1 mL;
    4. H_2 = 114 torr, NH_3 = 171 torr, CO_2 =
    229 torr, N_2 = 286 torr; 5. 0.395

12. 1. 0.12 moles; 2. 51 liters; 3. 28 atm;
    4. 154 K or -119° C; 5. 0.73 g/L;
    6. 29 g/mol; 7. 0.124 moles;
    8. 5290 L; 9. 59.0 g

13. 1. O; 2. H; 3. Cl; 4. Hg; 5. F; 6. Ba;
    7. He; 8. U; 9. Rn; 10. S; 11. Pu;
    12. Am; 13. Ra; 14. Ge; 15. Zn;
    16. As; 17. Pb; 18. Fe; 19. Ca;
    20. Co; 21. krypton; 22. potassium;
    23. carbon; 24. neon; 25. silicon;

26. zirconium; 27. tin; 28. platinum;
29. sodium; 30. aluminum;
31. copper; 32. silver; 33.
phosphorus; 34. manganese; 35.
iodine; 36. gold; 37. magnesium;
38. nickel; 39. bromine; 40. mercury

14. 1. 1, 1.0079, 1, 1, 0, 1; 2. 1, 1.0079, 1,
    1, 0, 0; 3. 6, 12.011, 12, 6, 6, 6; 4. 3,
    6.941, 7, 3, 4, 2; 5. 17, 35.453, 35, 17,
    18, 18; 6. 19, 39.0983, 39, 19, 20, 19;
    7. 12, 24.305, 24, 12, 12, 10; 8. 33,
    74.9216, 75, 33, 42, 36; 9. 47,
    107.868, 108, 47, 61, 47; 10. 47,
    107.868, 108, 47, 61, 46; 11. 16,
    32.06, 32, 16, 16, 18; 12. 92, 238.029,
    238, 92, 146, 92

15. 1. 126. 86 amu; 2. 197.5 amu;
    3. 55.85 amu; 4. 1.012 amu;
    5. 14.07 amu; 6. 12.04 amu

16. 1. $1s^2$ $2s^2$ $2p^6$ $3s^2$ $3p^5$

    ↑↓ ↑↓ ↑↓↑↓↑↓ ↑↓ ↑↓↑↓↑

    2. $1s^2$ $2s^2$ $2p^3$

    ↑↓ ↑↓ ↑ ↑ ↑

    3. $1s^2$ $2s^2$ $2p^6$ $3s^2$ $3p^1$

    ↑↓ ↑↓ ↑↓↑↓↑↓ ↑↓ ↑ _ _

    4. $1s^2$ $2s^2$ $2p^4$

    ↑↓ ↑↓ ↑↓↑ ↑ _ _

17. 1. 7; 2. 5; 3. 2; 4. 5; 5. 2; 6. 8; 7. 1;
    8. 2; 9. 2; 10. 6; 11. 1; 12. 2; 13. 4; 14.
    7; 15. 6; 16. 2; 17. 3; 18. 1; 19. 8; 20. 1

18. 1. $^{42}_{20}Ca$; 2. $^{235}_{92}U$; 3. ^4_2He; 4. ^4_2He; 5. ^3_1H;
    6. ^1_0N; 7. ^6_3Li; 8. $^{37}_{18}Ar$; 9. $^{235}_{92}U$; 10. $^{241}_{94}Pu$

19. 1. 12.5 g; 2. 7.2 seconds; 3. 23.4 g;
    4. 2.13 x 10^5 years; 5. 1$\overline{0}$0 g; 6. 160 g

20. 1. lower left; 2. upper right;
    3. decreased, increased positive
    nuclear charge; 4. increases,
    additional principal energy levels;
    5. larger; 6. smaller; 7. increases,
    increased positive nuclear charge;
    8. decreases, outermost electron is
    farther away from nucleus,
    shielding effect of inner electrons;
    9. upper right (F); 10. lower left (Fr);
    11. alkali metals

21. 12. alkaline earth metals;
13. transition elements; 14. metals,
nonmetals; 15. halogens;
16. fluorine; 17. nobel gases; 18. "d"
and "f"; 19. valence electrons;
20. principle energy levels;
21. transition element; 22. more;
23. metals; 24. atomic numbers;
25. semimetal or metalloid

22. 1. $K \cdot + \cdot \ddot{\underset{..}{F}} : \rightarrow K^+F^-$

2. $: \ddot{\underset{..}{I}} \cdot + \cdot Mg \cdot + \cdot \ddot{\underset{..}{I}} : \rightarrow Mg^{+2}I_2^-$

3. $Be : + \cdot \ddot{\underset{..}{S}} : \rightarrow Be^{+2}S^{-2}$

4. $Na \cdot + \cdot \ddot{\underset{..}{O}} \cdot + \cdot Na \rightarrow Na_2^+O^{-2}$

5. $: \ddot{\underset{..}{Br}} \cdot + \cdot \overset{\cdot \ddot{Br} :}{Al} \cdot + \cdot \ddot{\underset{..}{Br}} : \rightarrow Al^{+3}Br_3^-$

23. 1. $H \cdot + _x H \rightarrow$ (H$_x$H)

2. $: \ddot{F} \cdot + _x^{xx} F _x^x \rightarrow$ (: F $_x^{xx}$ F $_x^x$:)

3. $: \ddot{O} : + _x^x \ddot{O} _x^x \rightarrow$ (: Ö $_x^{xx}$ Ö $_x^x$)

4. $\cdot \ddot{N} : + _x^x N _x^x \rightarrow$ (N $_x^x$ N $_x^x$)

5. $: \ddot{O} : + _x C _x^x + : \ddot{O} : \rightarrow$ (: Ö $_x^{xx}$ C $_x^{xx}$ Ö :)

6. $H \cdot + _x^x \ddot{O} _x^x + \cdot H \rightarrow$ (H $_x$ Ö $_x^{xx}$ H)

24. 1. linear   2. bent

$: N \equiv N :$

3. linear   4. pyramidal

$: \ddot{O} = C = \ddot{O} :$

5. tetrahedral   6. triangular planar

7. linear   8. tetrahedral

$H - \ddot{\underset{..}{F}} :$ $H - \overset{H}{\underset{H}{C}} - \ddot{\underset{..}{O}} - H$

9. bent   10. linear

$: \ddot{I} - \ddot{I} :$

11. tetrahedral 12. linear

$: \ddot{\underset{..}{Cl}} - \overset{H}{\underset{: \ddot{Cl} :}{C}} - \ddot{\underset{..}{Cl}} :$ $: \ddot{O} = \ddot{O} :$

25. 1. nonpolar; 2. polar; 3. nonpolar;
4. polar; 5. nonpolar; 6. nonpolar;
7. polar; 8. polar; 9. polar;
10. nonpolar; 11. polar; 12. nonpolar

26. 1. NaCl, Na$_2$CO$_3$, NaOH, Na$_2$SO$_4$,
Na$_3$PO$_4$, NaNO$_3$; 2. NH$_4$Cl,
(NH$_4$)$_2$CO$_3$, NH$_4$OH, (NH$_4$)$_2$SO$_4$,
(NH$_4$)$_3$PO$_4$, NaNO$_3$; 3. KCl, K$_2$CO$_3$,
KOH, K$_2$SO$_4$, K$_3$PO$_4$, KNO$_3$; 4. CaCl$_2$,
CaCO$_3$, Ca(OH)$_2$, CaSO$_4$,
Ca$_3$(PO$_4$)$_2$, Ca(NO$_3$)$_2$; 5. MgCl$_2$,
MgCO$_3$, Mg(OH)$_2$, MgSO$_4$,
Mg$_3$(PO$_4$)$_2$, Mg(NO$_3$)$_2$; 6. ZnCl$_2$,
ZnCO$_3$, Zn(OH)$_2$, ZnSO$_4$, Zn$_3$(PO$_4$)$_2$,
Zn(NO$_3$)$_2$; 7. FeCl$_3$, Fe$_2$(CO$_3$)$_3$,
Fe(OH)$_3$, Fe$_2$(SO$_4$)$_3$, FePO$_4$, Fe(NO$_3$)$_3$;
8. AlCl$_3$, Al$_2$(CO$_3$)$_3$, Al(OH)$_3$, Al$_2$(SO$_4$)$_3$,
AlPO$_4$, Al(NO$_3$)$_3$; 9. CoCl$_3$,
Co$_2$(CO$_3$)$_3$, Co(OH)$_3$, Co$_2$(SO$_4$)$_3$,
CoPO$_4$, Co(NO$_3$)$_3$; 10. FeCl$_2$, FeCO$_3$,
Fe(OH)$_2$, FeSO$_4$, Fe$_3$(PO$_4$)$_2$, Fe(NO$_3$)$_2$;
11. HCl, H$_2$CO$_3$, HOH or H$_2$O, H$_2$SO$_4$,
H$_3$PO$_4$, HNO$_3$

27. 1. calcium carbonate; 2. potassium
chloride; 3. iron (II) sulfate; 4. lithium
bromide; 5. magnesium chloride;
6. iron (III) chloride; 7. zinc
phosphate; 8. ammonium nitrate;
9. aluminum hydroxide; 10. copper
(I) acetate; 11. lead (II) sulfate;
12. sodium chlorate; 13. calcium
oxalate; 14. iron (III) oxide;
15. ammonium phosphate;
16. sodium hydrogen sulfate (or
sodium bisulfate); 17. mercury (I)
chloride; 18. magnesium nitrate;

19. copper (II) sulfate; 20. sodium hydrogen carbonate (or sodium bicarbonate); 21. nickel (III) bromide; 22. beryllium nitrate; 23. zinc sulfate; 24. gold (III) chloride; 25. potassium permanganate

28. 1. carbon dioxide; 2. carbon monoxide; 3. sulfur dioxide; 4. sulfur trioxide; 5. dinitrogen monoxide; 6. nitrogen monoxide; 7. dinitrogen trioxide; 8. nitrogen dioxide; 9. dinitrogen tetroxide; 10. dinitrogen pentoxide; 11. phosphorus trichloride; 12. phosphorus pentachloride; 13. ammonia; 14. sulfur hexachloride; 15. diphosphorus pentoxide; 16. carbon tetrachloride; 17. silicon dioxide; 18. carbon disulfide; 19. oxygen difluoride; 20. phosphorus tribromide

29. 1. nitric acid; 2. hydrochloric acid; 3. sulfuric acid; 4. sulfurous acid; 5. acetic acid; 6. hydrobromic acid; 7. nitrous acid; 8. phosphoric acid; 9. hydrosulfuric acid; 10. carbonic acid; 11. H_2SO_4; 12. HNO_3; 13. HCl; 14. $HC_2H_3O_2$; 15. HF; 16. H_3PO_3; 17. H_2CO_3; 18. HNO_2; 19. H_3PO_4; 20. H_2S

30. 1. $(NH_4)PO_4$; 2. FeO; 3. Fe_2O_3; 4. CO; 5. $CaCl_2$; 6. KNO_3; 7. $Mg(OH)_2$; 8. $Al_2(SO_4)_3$; 9. $CuSO_4$; 10. $Pb(CrO_4)_2$; 11. P_2O_5; 12. $KMnO_4$; 13. $NaHCO_3$; 14. $Zn(NO_3)_2$; 15. $Al_2(SO_3)_3$

31. 1. 158 g; 2. 74.55 g; 3. 142 g; 4. 164 g; 5. 342 g; 6. 149 g; 7. 250 g; 8. 262.86 g; 9. 219 g; 10. 458 g; 11. 62 g; 12. 617 g; 13. 304 g; 14. 352 g; 15. 77 g

32. 1. 0.43 mole; 2. 1.28 moles; 3. 0.633 mole; 4. 0.99 mole; 5. 0.14 mole; 6. 145 g; 7. 49 g; 8. 269 g; 9. 19 g; 10. 800 g

33. 1. 22.4 L; 2. 71.7 L; 3. 16.8 L; 4. 39.2 L; 5. 11.2 L; 6. 56 L; 7. 70.0 L; 8. 22.4 L; 9. 31 L; 10. 13 L

34. 1. 1.2×10^{24}; 2. 9.0×10^{23}; 3. 4.5×10^{23}; 4. 9.0×10^{24}; 5. 2.1×10^{23}; 6. 1.00; 7. 2.00; 8. 0.00025; 9. 560; 10. 0.00012

35. 1. 1.1×10^3 g; 2. 5.6×10^2 liters; 3. 2.02×10^{24} molecules; 4. 56.9 g; 5. 3.9×10^{22} atoms; 6. 3.5 liters; 7. 1.9×10^{23} atoms, 9.4×10^{22} molecules

36. 1. 24.7% K, 34.8% Mn, 40.5% O; 2. 2.8% H, 97.2% Cl; 3. 16.2% Mg, 18.9% N, 64.9% O; 4. 28.2% N, 8.1% H, 20.8% P, 42.9% O; 5. 15.8% Al, 28.1% S, 56.1% O; 6. 39.3 g O; 7. 17.5 g; 8. 109 g Ag

37. 1. CH_4; 2. KCl; 3. $AlPO_4$; 4. $MgBr_2$; 5. Na_2SO_4; 6. $CuSO_4 \bullet 5H_2O$

38. 1. N_2O_4; 2. C_5H_{10}; 3. $C_2H_4O_2$ (CH_3COOH); 4. $C_4H_{10}O$ (C_4H_9OH); 5. $C_4H_8O_2$ (C_3H_7COOH)

39. 1. 36%; 2. 67.5%; 3. 14%; 4. 32%; 5. 2.6 g; 6. 3

40. 1. $N_2 + 3H_2 \rightarrow 2NH_3$
2. $2KClO_3 \rightarrow 2KCl + 3O_2$
3. $2NaCl + Fe \rightarrow 2NaF + Cl_2$
4. $2H_2 + O_2 \rightarrow 2H_2O$
5. $2AgNO_3 + MgCl_2 \rightarrow 2AgCl + Mg(NO_3)_2$
6. $2AlBr_3 + 3K_2SO_4 \rightarrow 6KBr + Al_2(SO_4)_3$
7. $CH_4 + 2O_2 \rightarrow CO_2 + 2H_2O$
8. $C_3H_8 + 5O_2 \rightarrow 3CO_2 + 4H_2O$
9. $2C_8H_{18} + 25O_2 \rightarrow 16CO_2 + 18H_2O$
10. $FeCl_3 + 3NaOH \rightarrow Fe(OH)_3 + 3NaCl$
11. $4P + 5O_2 \rightarrow 2P_2O_5$
12. $2Na + 2H_2O \rightarrow 2NaOH + H_2$
13. $2Ag_2O \rightarrow 4Ag + O_2$
14. $S_8 + 12O_2 \rightarrow 8SO_3$
15. $6CO_2 + 6H_2O \rightarrow C_6H_{12}O_6 + 6O_2$
16. $2K + MgBr_2 \rightarrow 2KBr + Mg$
17. $2HCl + CaCO_3 \rightarrow CaCl_2 + H_2O + CO_2$

41. 1. $Zn + Pb(NO_3)_2 \rightarrow Zn(NO_3)_2 + Pb$
2. $2AlBr_3 + 3Cl_2 \rightarrow 2AlCl_3 + 3Br_2$
3. $2Na_3PO_4 + 3CaCl_2 \rightarrow Ca_3(PO_4)_2 + 6NaCl$
4. $2KClO_3 + 2KCl \rightarrow 3O_2(g)$
5. $2Al + 6HCl \rightarrow 2AlCl_3 + 3H_2(g)$
6. $3Ca(OH)_2 + 2H_3PO_4 \rightarrow Ca_3(PO_4)_2 + 6H_2O$

7. $Cu + 2H_2SO_4 \rightarrow CuSO_4 + 2H_2O + SO_2$

8. $2H_2 + 2NO \rightarrow 2H_2O + N_2$

42. 1. synthesis; 2. decomposition; 3. cationic single replacement; 4. synthesis; 5. decomposition; 6. anionic single replacement; 7. synthesis; 8. double replacement; 9. decomposition; 10. double replacement

43. 1. $MgBr_2 + Cl_2 \rightarrow MgCl_2 + Br_2$, anionic single replacement

2. $Al + Fe_2O_3 \rightarrow Fe + Al_2 + O_3$, cationic single replacement

3. $2AgNO_3 + ZnCl_2 \rightarrow AgCl + Zn(NO_3)_2$, double replacement

4. $2H_2O_2 \xrightarrow{MnO_2} 2H_2O + O_2$, decomposition

5. $Zn + 2HCl \rightarrow ZnCl_2 + H_2$, cationic single replacement

6. $H_2SO_4 + 2NaOH \rightarrow Na_2SO_4 + 2H_2O$, double replacement (neutralization)

7. $2NA + H_2 \rightarrow 2NaH$, synthesis

8. $CH_3COOH + Cu$ (or $HC_2H_3O_2$) $\rightarrow$ no reaction, cationic single replacement

44. 1. 6 moles; 2. 9 moles; 3. 3 moles; 4. 20 moles; 5. 6 moles

45. 1. 15 liters; 2. 10 liters; 3. 12 liters; 4. 15 mL; 5. 75 L, 37.5 L

46. 1. 15 g; 2. 10.7 g; 3. 60.7 g; 4. 4.2 g; 5. 3.1 g

47. 1. 40.0 L; 2. 1.4 L; 3. 3.0 g; 4. 0.86 L; 5. 8.5×10^{21} molecules; 6. 6.77×10^{22} molecules

48. 1. 34 g; 2. 19 g; 3. 23 L; 4. 25.0 g; 5. 164 g; 6. 136 g

49. 1. $KClO_3$; 2. 100 g; 3. 180 g; 4. NaCl; 5. unsaturated; 6. 22 g; 7. NH_3; 8. KI; 9. $KClO_3$; 10. NaCl

50. 1. 1.0 M; 2. 0.118 M; 3. 101 g; 4. 270 mL; 5. 2.5 g

51. 1. 2.0 m; 2. 0.22 m; 3. 0.12 m; 4. 3.8 g; 5. 135 g

52. 1. 2.0 N; 2. 6.0 N; 3. 1.5 M; 4. 0.054 N;

5. 13.3 g

53. 1. electrolyte; 2. nonelectrolyte; 3. nonelectrolyte; 4. electrolyte; 5. nonelectrolyte; 6. electrolyte; 7. nonelectrolyte; 8. electrolyte; 9. electrolyte; 10. electrolyte

54. 1. 100.45° C; 2. -1.6°C; 3. 108.4°C; 4. 149 g

55. 1. water; 2. CCl_4, alcohol; 3. water, CCl_4, alcohol; 4. CCl_4, alcohol; 5. CCl_4, alcohol; 6. water; 7. CCl_4, alcohol; 8. water

56. 1. exothermic; 2. B; 3. F; 4. D; 5. A; 6. E; 7. C; 8. endothermic; 9. A, C, E

57. 1. increase; 2. decrease; 3. decrease; 4. increase; 5. increase; 6. increase; 7. decrease; 8. increase; 9. no change; 10. decrease; 11. increase; 12. decrease; 13. decrease; 14. no change; 15. decrease

58. 1. negative, positive; 2. positive, negative; 3. enthalpy, entropy; 4. always; 5. never; 6. sometimes; 7. -7,360 kJ; 8. yes; 9. +1,460 kJ

59. 1.
$$K = \frac{[NH_3]^2}{[N_2][CH_2]^3}$$

2.
$$K = [O_2]^3$$

3.
$$K = [H^+][OH^-]$$

4.
$$K = \frac{[CO_2]^2}{[CO]^2[O_2]}$$

5.
$$K = [Li^+]^2[CO_3^{-2}]$$

60. 2. right, decrease, --, increase, same; 3. left, increase, increase, ---, same; 4. left, ---, increase, decrease, same; 5. left, increase, ---, decrease, same; 6. right, decrease, decrease, --, same;

7. left, increase, increase, decrease, decrese; 8. right, decrease, decrease, increase, increase; 9. right, decrease, decrease, increase, same; 10. left, increase, increase, decrease, same

61. 1. $H_2O + H_2O \leftrightarrow H_3O^+ + OH^-$
    2. $H_2SO_4^- + OH^- \leftrightarrow HSO_4^- + H_2O$
    3. $HSO_4 + H_2O \leftrightarrow SO_4^{-2} + H_3O^+$
    4. $OH^- + H_3O^+ \leftrightarrow H_2O + H_2O$
    5. $NH_3 + H_2O \leftrightarrow HN_4^+ + OH^-$

62. 2. $H_2PO_4^-, H_3PO_4 \leftrightarrow H^+ + H_2PO_4^-$
    3. $HF, HF \leftrightarrow H^+ + F^-$
    4. $HNO_3, HNO_3 \leftrightarrow H^+ + NO_3^-$
    5. $HPO_4^{-2}, H_2PO_4^- \leftrightarrow H^+ + HPO_4^{-2}$
    6. $OH^-, H_2O \leftrightarrow H^+ + OH^-$
    7. $HSO_4^-, HSO_4^- \leftrightarrow H^+ + SO_4^{-2}$
    8. $PO_4^{-3}, HPO_4^{-2} \leftrightarrow H^+ + PO_4^{-3}$
    9. $NH_3, NH_4^+ \leftrightarrow H^+ + NH_3$
    10. $H_3O^+, H_3O \leftrightarrow H^+ + H_2O$

63. 2. 10^{-7} M, 10^{-7}, 7, Neutral; 3. 10^{-10} M, 10, 4, Basic; 4. 2, 10^{-12} M, 12, Acidic; 5. 10^{-3} M, 3, 10^{-11} M, Acidic; 6. 10^{-12} M, 10^{-2} M, 2, Basic; 7. 10^{-9} M, 9, 5, Basic; 8. 11, 10^{-3} M, 3, Basic; 9. 10^{-1} M, 1, 10^{-13} M, Acidic; 10. 10^{-6} M, 10^{-8} M, 8, Acidic

64. 1. 1.2 N, 1.2 M; 2. 0.68 M, 1.4 N; 3. $1\overline{0}0$ mL; 4. 5 mL; 5. 0.01 M

65. 1. HCl, KOH, neutral; 2. HNO_3, NH_4OH ($NH_3 + H_2O$), acidic; 3. H_3PO_4, NaOH, basic; 4. H_2SO_4, $Ca(OH)_2$, neutral; 5. HBr, $Al(OH)_3$, acidic; 6. HI, $Cu(OH)_2$, acidic; 7. $Mg(OH)_2$, HF, basic; 8. HNO_3, NaOH, neutral; 9. $HC_2H_3O_2$, LiOH, basic; 10. HCl, $Zn(OH)_2$, acidic; 11. H_2SO_4, $Sr(OH)_2$, neutral; 12. H_3PO_4, $Ba(OH)_2$, basic

66. 1. +1, −1; 2. +1, +5, −2; 3. −2, +1; 4. +2, −3; 5. +1, +5, −2; 6. +3, +5, −2;

7. 0; 8. +1, −1; 9. +4, −2; 10. +1, +1, +6, −2; 11. +1, +4, −2; 12. +1, +6, −2; 13. +2, −1; 14. +1, +7, −2; 15. +1, −1; 16. +4, −2; 17. +2, −1; 18. +6, −2; 19. −3, +1; 20. 0

67. 1. $2H_2 + O_2 \rightarrow 2H_2O$
    (reducing agent / oxidizing agent)
    ox. hr: $2H_2° \rightarrow 4H^+ + He^-$
    red. hr: $He^- + O_2° \rightarrow 2O^{-2}$

    2. $Fe + Zn^{2+} \rightarrow Fe^{2+} + Zn$
    (reducing agent / oxidizing agent)
    ox. hr: $Fe \rightarrow Fe^{2+} + 2e^-$
    red. hr: $2e^- + Zn^{2+} \rightarrow Zn°$

    3. $2Al + 3Fe^{+2} \rightarrow 2Al^{+3} + 3Fe$
    (reducing agent / oxidizing agent)
    ox. hr: $2Al° \rightarrow 2Al^{+3} + 6e^-$
    red. hr: $6e^- + 3Fe^{+2} \rightarrow 3Fe°$

    4. $Cu + 2AgNO_3 \rightarrow Cu(NO_3)_2 + 2Ag$
    (reducing agent / oxidizing agent)
    ox. hr: $Cu° \rightarrow Cu^{+2} + 2e^-$
    red. hr: $2e^- + 2Ag^+ \rightarrow 2Ag°$

68. 1. $Sn° + 2Ag^+ \rightarrow Sn^{+2} + 2Ag°$
    ox: $Sn° \rightarrow Sn^{+2} + 2e^-$
    red: $2(e^- + Ag^+ \rightarrow Ag°)$
    2. $2Cr° + 3Pb^{2+} \rightarrow 2Cr^{+3} + 3Pb°$
    ox: $2(Cr° \rightarrow Cr^{+3} + 3e^-)$
    red: $3(2e^- + Pb^{2+} \rightarrow Pb°)$
    3. $2KClO_3 \rightarrow 2KCl + 3O_2$
    ox: $2O_3^{-2} \rightarrow 3O_2° + 12e^-$
    red: $2(6e^- + Cl^{+5} \rightarrow Cl^-)$
    4. $4NH_3 + 5O_2 \rightarrow 4NO + 6H_2O$
    ox: $4(N^{-3} \rightarrow N^{+2} + 5e^-)$
    red: $5(He^- + O_2 \rightarrow 2O^{-2})$
    5. $PbS + 4H_2O_2 \rightarrow PbSO_4 + 4H_2O$
    ox: $S^{-2} \rightarrow S^{+6} \rightarrow 8e^-$
    red: $4(2e^- + O_2^{-1} \rightarrow 2O^{-2})$
    6. $3H_2S + 2HNO_3 \rightarrow 3S + 2NO + 4H_2O$
    ox: $3(S^{-2} \rightarrow S° + 2e^-)$
    red: $2(3e^- + N^{+5} \rightarrow N^{+2})$
    7. $MnO_2 + H_2C_2O_4 + H_2SO_4 \rightarrow MnSO_4 + 2CO_2 + 2H_2O$
    ox: $C_2^{+6} \rightarrow 2C^{+4} + 2e^-$
    red: $2e^- + Mn^{+4} \rightarrow Mn^{+2}$
    8. $2H_2S + H_2SO_3 \rightarrow 3S + 3H_2O$

ox: $2(S^{-2} \rightarrow S^\circ + 2e^-)$
red: $4e^- + S^{+4} \rightarrow S^\circ$
9. $KIO_3 + 3H_2SO_3 \rightarrow KI + 3H_2SO_4$
ox: $3(S^{+4} \rightarrow S^{+6} + 2e^-)$
red: $6e^- + I^{+5} \rightarrow I^-$
10. $K_2Cr_2O_7 + 14HCl \rightarrow 2KCl + 2CrCl_3 + 3Cl_2 + 7H_2O$
ox: $3(2Cl^- \rightarrow Cl_2^\circ + 2e^-)$
red: $6e^- + Cr_2^{+6} \rightarrow 2Cr^{+3}$

69. 1. aluminum; 2. $2Al^\circ + 3Pb^{+2} \rightarrow 2Al^{+3} + 3Pb^\circ$; 3. +1.53 V; 4. from aluminum to lead; 5. from aluminum nitrate to lead (II) nitrate; 6. aluminum; 7. lead; 8. increasing; 9. decreasing; 10. zero; 11. aluminum; 12. lead; 13. lead; 14. aluminum

70. 1. propane; 2. n-butene or 1-butene; 3. propyne; 4. 2-methyl pentane; 5. butane; 6. methyl propane or isobutane; 7. 2-pentene; 8. 3, 3-diethylpentane

71.

72. 1. carboxylic acid 2. ketone
3. alcohol 4. ether

5. aldehyde 6. alcohol

7. carboxylic acid 8. ester

9. ketone 10. ether

73. 1. ethanol; 2. propanone; 3. butanal; 4. ethanoic acid (acetic acid); 5. dimethyl ether, 6. methyl ethanoate or methyl acetate; 7. 2-butanol; 8. propanoic acid; 9. ethanol; 10. 2-butanone

74.